WHAT IS MATHS?

Maths is more than just adding up, taking away, multiplying and dividing. Maths is more than just numbers! Maths is part of everybody's daily life, from spending money and checking your change, to following a recipe correctly – even finding patterns in the world and sharing properly with your friends.

WHAT IS STEM?

STEM stands for 'science, technology, engineering and mathematics (maths)'. These four areas are closely linked: new discoveries in science give technology and engineering new things to invent to make our lives easier and the world a better place. However, you could say that mathematics is the most important one as no scientist or engineer could do their job properly without it!

Science   Technology   Engineering   Maths

MEASURING AND GUESSING

There are lots of ways to measure lengths. You can use a ruler or tape measure to measure accurately, or you can estimate – which is a bit like clever guessing. Estimating takes practice but there are some tricks to help you.

Take a look at these shapes and use the guide to estimate their sizes. The pencils and tomatoes are the correct size on the page so you can use a ruler to check your estimate.

Symbols

=

This sign means 'equal to' and is used when measuring accurately.

≈

This sign means 'approximately equal to' and is used when estimating measurements.

Guide

1 cm ≈ the width of a pencil

3 cm ≈ the length of a cherry tomato

30 cm ≈ the height of a sheet of A4 paper

1 m ≈ the width of a single bed

2 m ≈ the height of a door in a house

Estimate : 6cm

Measurement: 6cm

Estimate: 5 cm

Measurement: ~~3 cm~~
5 cm

How do your estimates measure up?

Estimate: 3 m

SHOPPING

Going shopping involves maths! You need to add together your money to check you have enough to buy everything and to give the cashier the right amount.

Check the prices of everything on your shopping list against the money you have in your pocket. On your shopping list, write down how much each will cost and which coins you'll need. Put a cross over each coin when you've used it.
Answers on page 30!

5p

10p

10p

10p

20p

20p

20p

25p 25p
£1
25p 25p

50p

50p

50p

2 lemons ✓ 40P

4 bananas £1·14P

1 pint of milk 50P

1 loaf of bread 80P
75P

3 apples 15 +15
75

AT THE POST OFFICE

Bigger things aren't necessarily heavier than smaller things. A pillow filled with feathers is larger than a brick, but the brick is heavier. We can measure weight by using scales, and the metric scale measures in grams (g) and kilograms (kg). There are 1,000 grams in a kilogram.

Check the scales for each of these parcels and write their weights in the spaces provided.
Answers on page 30!
What do you think is in each box?
Draw your answers!

Here are some sample weights to give you ideas. But you can also weigh items around you and choose things to put in the parcels that are not on this list.

Remember this little symbol? ≈

a packet of crisps ≈ 35g
a tennis ball ≈ 50g
a DVD in its case ≈ 100g
a mobile phone ≈ 150g
a cricket ball ≈ 175g
an exercise book ≈ 200g
a football ≈ 440g
a small bag of sugar ≈ 500g

1.

1kg/0kg

900 925 950 975   25 50 75 **100**
875   125
850   150
825   175
800   **200**
775   225
750   250
725   275
700   **300**
675   325
650   350
625   375
600 575   425 **400**
       550 525 475 450
          500

g

TAKE AWAYS

Things are taken away – or subtracted – in all sorts of everyday situations.
Some things are simple to count, if they are all the same size and shape, such as
squares of a chocolate bar. Other things, like liquids, have to be measured in
fractions (or equal parts) of a whole unit. The whole unit could be an official
way of measuring, such as litres, or anything useful, like a bottle or cup.

For each of these
objects, shade in the
amount that has been
taken away or used up,
and write down the
amount left.

Someone has
eaten 7 squares.
Amount left: 23

A quarter of the
bottle has been used.
Amount left: not much

3/4

1/2

1/4

6 pins have been
knocked over
Amount left:
4

10

Subtract all the spaces with a dot marked in them by colouring them in — and you'll find a picture revealed in the space left behind.

VOLUME

Capacity – also called 'volume' – is a measure of how much space something takes up. You can measure the capacity of things that can be poured from one container to another. Capacity can be measured in millilitres (ml) and litres (l), and there are 1,000 millilitres in a litre. However, you might see capacity measured in all sorts of ways.

Here are some common ways capacity is measured:

a pinch

a drop

a teaspoon

a tablespoon

a cup

In this recipe, some of the ingredients are measured in weight, and some are measured in volume. Circle the words that are telling you what volume to use.

Clue: Remember — volume isn't always measured in just millilitres and litres.

Vanilla cupcakes

110g butter

110g caster sugar

2 free-range eggs

1 teaspoon vanilla extract

110g self-raising flour

1-2 tablespoons milk

Buttercream icing

140g butter

280g icing sugar

1-2 tablespoons milk

a few drops food colouring

Decorate these cupcakes!

1. Preheat the oven to 180° C (350° F) or Gas Mark 4 and line a muffin tin with paper cases (ask an adult to help you).

2. Cream the butter and sugar together then slowly beat in the eggs and vanilla extract.

3. Carefully mix in the flour adding little drops of milk as you go.

4. Bake for 10-15 minutes until golden on top then leave to cool.

5. Beat the butter for the icing until soft then add half of the icing sugar and beat some more.

6. Add the rest of the icing sugar and the milk to the butter and mix until smooth.

7. Decorate your cupcakes! Use food colouring in the icing for a special finish.

13

MULTIPLES

Multiplication is adding the same number to itself an amount of times. So, 3 x 3 means to add 3 to itself three times, or 3 + 3 + 3.

You can represent 3 x 3 in a grid, too, where there are 3 rows and 3 columns, like this:

or 2 x 4 like this:

And counting the number of squares gives you the answer to the question.

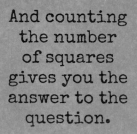

Use the pictures opposite to help you solve these multiplication questions.
Look for the boxes that match the number of rows and columns in the question.

2 X 5 = [ ]   5 X 6 = [ ]

3 X 6 = [ ]   8 X 9 = [ ]

4 X 5 = [ ]   9 X 10 = [ ]

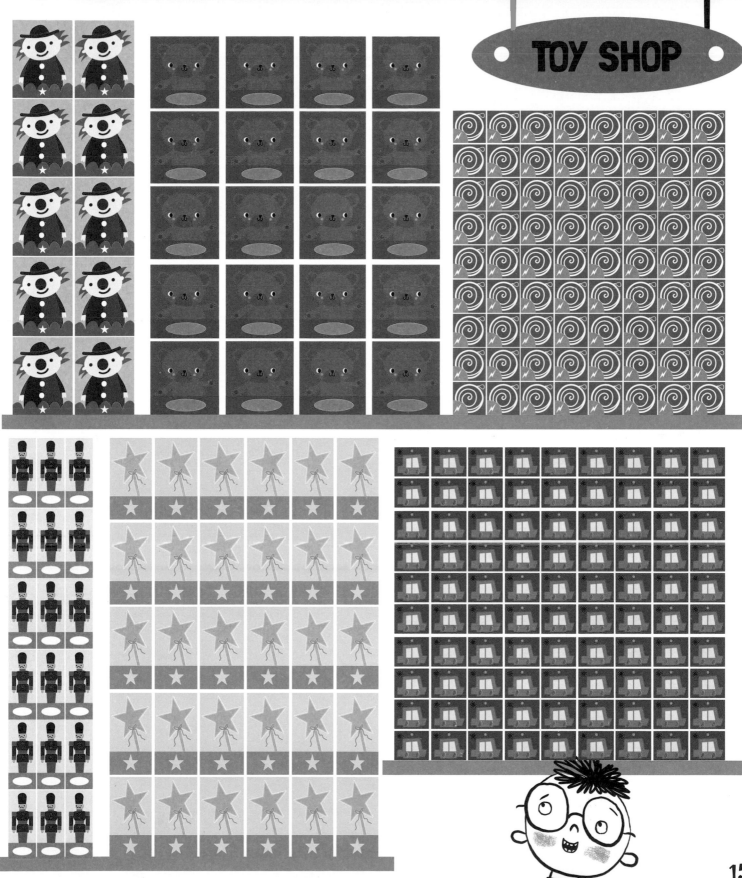

TOY SHOP

15

RACING MATHS

It's important to know how to measure time. Telling the time helps you arrive at school on time and helps your teacher make sure your lessons last the right amount of time. People running races also need to measure time to know exactly how long they have taken. Time can be measured in seconds, minutes and hours. There are 60 seconds in a minute and 60 minutes in an hour.

Can you help the referee measure the time for each runner? The referee has only noted Caden's time, and how much faster or slower than Caden the others were. Write their times down on the referee's pad.

Caden
65 seconds

Daniel
+ 7 seconds

Evie
+ 12 seconds

SHARING

Sharing things out is called 'division'. Things can be shared out evenly but sometimes there will be leftovers known as the remainder.

These cakes have all been cut into different numbers of slices. First, count the number of slices, then use different coloured pencils to share out the slices equally amongst the number of guests listed for each cake. Each guest can have more than one slice of cake but they must all have the same number of slices each. Here's one to start you off.

Number of slices: 8
Share between 4 guests
Slices left over: 0

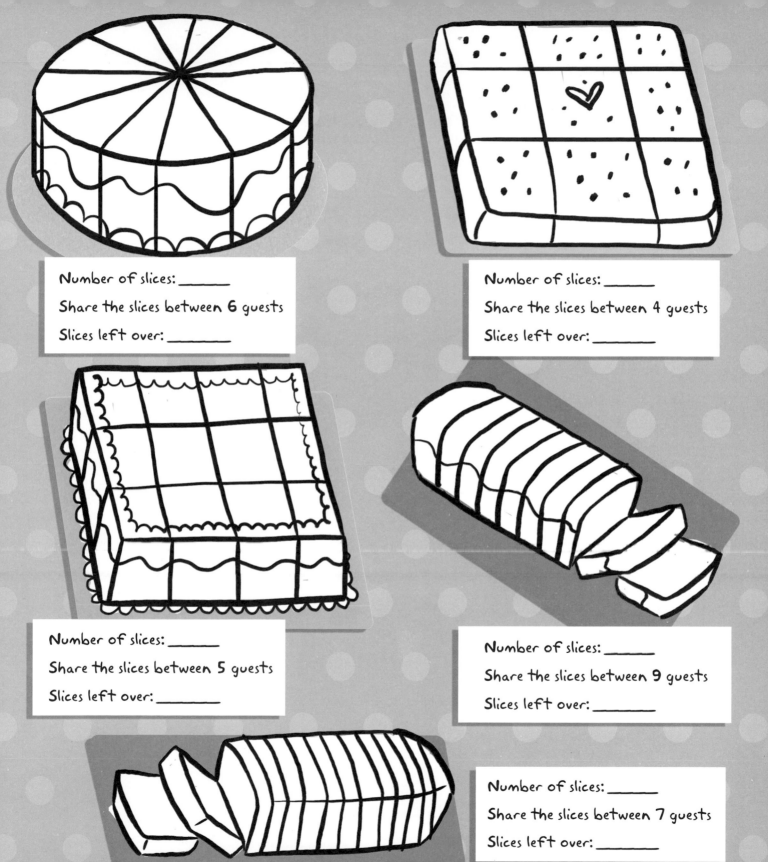

Number of slices: _____
Share the slices between 6 guests
Slices left over: _____

Number of slices: _____
Share the slices between 4 guests
Slices left over: _____

Number of slices: _____
Share the slices between 5 guests
Slices left over: _____

Number of slices: _____
Share the slices between 9 guests
Slices left over: _____

Number of slices: _____
Share the slices between 7 guests
Slices left over: _____

19

which helps you decipher the code. There are many different ways to write code. Some are quite famous, but the hardest to crack are the ones that are made up specially with secret rules that only a very small number of people know.

Here are some famous codes. For each one, use the key to decode the secret messages.

THE REVERSE ALPHABET

The clue's in the title! The code is simply the reverse of the alphabet. This code is easy to crack but that also means you'll never forget how to crack it, even if you lose your key.

A	B	C	D	E	F	G	H	I	J	K	L	M	N	O	P	Q	R	S	T	U	V	W	X	Y	Z
Z	Y	X	W	V	U	T	S	R	Q	P	O	N	M	L	K	J	I	H	G	F	E	D	C	B	A

D	S	Z	G		R	H		U	L	I		W	R	M	M	V	I	?

WHAT IS FOR DINNER?

AUGUSTUS'S CODE

Another simple code, this time the alphabet is all shifted on one place, so that A=B, B=C, and so on until Z=A.
This message uses the bottom line of the code.

A	B	C	D	E	F	G	H	I	J	K	L	M	N	O	P	Q	R	S	T	U	V	W	X	Y	Z
Z	A	B	C	D	E	F	G	H	I	J	K	L	M	N	O	P	Q	R	S	T	U	V	W	X	Y

Z	T	F	T	R	S	T	R		V	Z	R		Z		Q	N	L	Z	M

AUGUSTUS WAS A ROMAN

20

PICTOGRAM CODE

You don't always need to use letters in your code!
Pictograms, or little pictures, can take the place of letters.

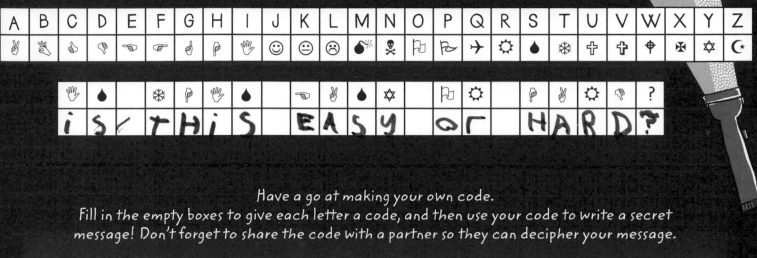

A	B	C	D	E	F	G
Z	Y	X	W	V	U	T

H	I	J	K	L	M	N
S	R	Q	P	O	N	N

O	P	Q	R	S	T	U
L	K	J	I	H	G	f

V	W	X	Y	Z
E	D			

Have a go at making your own code.
Fill in the empty boxes to give each letter a code, and then use your code to write a secret
message! Don't forget to share the code with a partner so they can decipher your message.

TURN THE TABLES

Making notes of the things we see can help us to see patterns. Writing stuff down helps us to take more notice.

Look at this scene and record information about it in the table by putting ticks in the right boxes. The first line has been filled in for you.

	Mum	Dad	brother	sister	baby
eating cereal			✓	✓	✓
eating toast					
curly hair					
straight hair					
wearing red					
smiling					
drinking juice					
drinking milk					

BAR CHARTS

Tables gather numbers in a grid. Bar charts are a fun way to turn this information into something visual. A 'bar' on the chart represents the number value in the table.

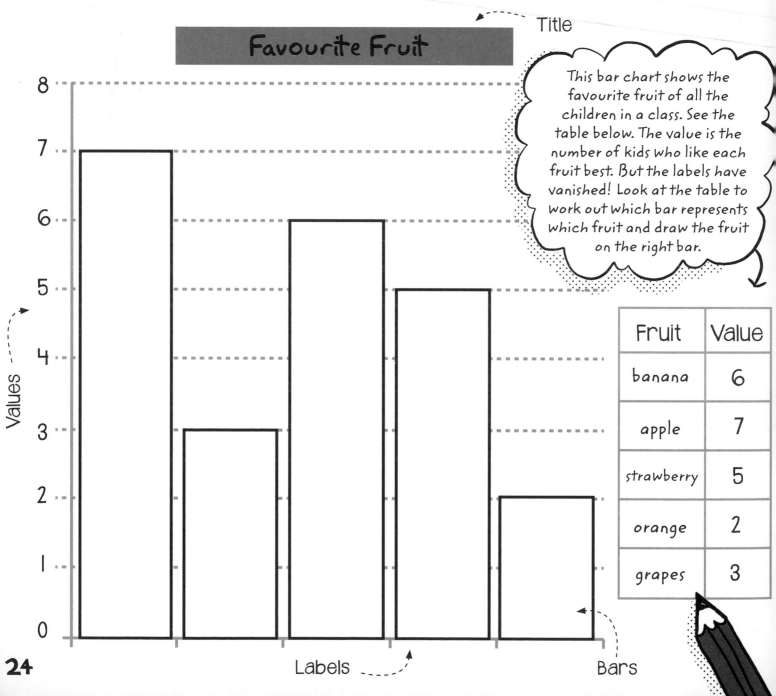

Title

Favourite Fruit

This bar chart shows the favourite fruit of all the children in a class. See the table below. The value is the number of kids who like each fruit best. But the labels have vanished! Look at the table to work out which bar represents which fruit and draw the fruit on the right bar.

Fruit	Value
banana	6
apple	7
strawberry	5
orange	2
grapes	3

Values

Labels

Bars

Victor gathered this information about his friends' favourite hobbies. Use a pencil and ruler to turn the information in this table into a bar chart.

Hobby	Value
football	8
ballet	4
swimming	5
karate	2
scouts	5

8

7

6

5

4

3

2

1

0

RIGHT ANGLES

When two straight lines meet they make an angle. A 'right angle' is a special kind of angle, shaped like an 'L' – once you can recognise a right angle you'll see they are all around us.

See if you can find six right angles in this picture. Circle all the ones you can find.

ROUNDING UP

Sometimes it's easier to understand larger numbers if they are rounded up or down to something simpler.

Numbers 1 to 4 are rounded down to the nearest 0. So 13 becomes 10.

Numbers 5 to 9 are rounded up to the nearest 0. So 27 becomes 30.

You can also round off numbers and use other words to describe numbers. Here are some words you can use to describe a number without saying the exact number.

roughly

more than

almost

less than

nearly

close to

about

In these conversations, reply to the friend talking in exact numbers with another way of describing the number, rounded off. Use the words suggested on the opposite page to help you.

I have 97 action figures!

You have nearly 100 action figures!

I can skip 32 times without stopping!

I am 8 years and 11 months old.

I scored a basket 11 times in a row!

There are 26 pupils in my class.

ANSWERS

Pages 4-5

Pencils
Estimate : **6 cm**
Measurement : **6.3 cm**

Punnet of cherry tomatoes
Estimate : **15 cm**
Measurement : **15.3 cm**

House
Estimate : **6 m**

Pages 6-7

2 lemons = 40p (2 x 20p)

4 bananas = £1 (1 x £1)

1 pint of milk = 50p (1 x 50p)

1 loaf of bread = 80p (1 x 50p, 1 x 20p, 1 x 10p)

3 apples = 75p (1 x 50p, 2 x 10p, 1 x 5p)

Page 8-9

Here are the weights showing on the scales and some ideas for what could be inside the parcels. You might have chosen other things to go in the parcels by weighing items around you.

1. The scale shows 100g = a DVD in its case
2. The scale shows 175g = a cricket ball
3. The scale shows 250g = an exercise book + a tennis ball
4. The scale shows 475g = a football + a packet of crisps
5. The scale shows 650g = a small bag of sugar + a mobile phone

Page 10

Chocolate bar	Bottle of laundry liquid	Bowling pins
Amount left: 23	Amount left: 3/4	Amount left: 4

30

Page 11

Page 12

Vanilla cupcakes

110g butter

110g caster sugar

2 free-range eggs

1 teaspoon vanilla extract

110g self-raising flour

1-2 tablespoons milk

Buttercream icing

140g butter

280g icing sugar

1-2 tablespoons milk

a few drops food colouring

Page 14-15

$2 \times 5 = 10$

$3 \times 6 = 18$

$4 \times 5 = 20$

$5 \times 6 = 30$

$8 \times 9 = 72$

$9 \times 10 = 90$

Page 18-19

Cake 1

Number of slices: 12

Slices left over: 0

Cake 2

Number of slices: 9

Slices left over: 1

Cake 3

Number of slices: 12

Slices left over: 2

Cake 4

Number of slices: 10

Slices left over: 1

Cake 5

Number of slices: 14

Slices left over: 0

Page 16-17

1st : Ahmed 55 seconds

2nd : Betty 1 minute

3rd : Caden 1 minute 5 seconds

4th : Daniel 1 minute 12 seconds

5th : Evie 1 minute 17 seconds

Page 22-23

Reverse Alphabet: What is for dinner?

Augustus's Code: Augustus was a Roman

Pictogram Code: Is this easy or hard?

Page 22-23

	Mum	Dad	brother	sister	baby
eating cereal			✔	✔	✔
eating toast	✔	✔			
curly hair	✔		✔		
straight hair		✔		✔	
wearing red			✔		✔
smiling	✔		✔		✔
drinking juice				✔	✔
drinking milk					✔

Page 26-27

There are 8 right angles in the picture.

Page 24-25

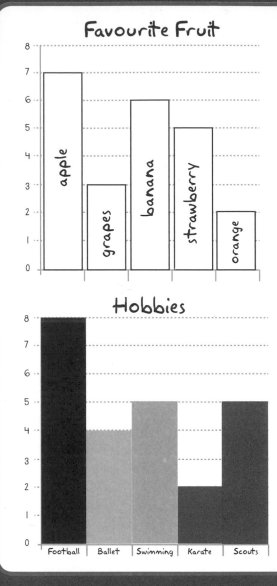

Favourite Fruit

Hobbies

Page 28-29

Possible answers:

- You can skip more than 30 times!
- You are nearly 9 years old.
- You have scored more than 10 baskets in a row.
- You have close to 30 pupils in your class.

32